Tree-HOUSE COMIX Proudly Presents

DOG MAN
BRAWL of the WILD

WRITTEN AND ILLUSTRATED BY **DAV PILKEY**

AS GEORGE BEARD AND HAROLD HUTCHINS

WITH COLOR BY JOSE GARIBALDI

graphix

AN IMPRINT OF

SCHOLASTIC

FOR LIZETTE SERRANO
THANK YOU FOR YOUR STRENGTH,
COMPASSION, AND DEVOTION
TO LIBRARIES AND KIDS

Scholastic Children's Books
An imprint of Scholastic Ltd
Euston House, 24 Eversholt Street, London, NW1 1DB, UK
Registered office: Westfield Road, Southam, Warwickshire, CV47 0RA
SCHOLASTIC and associated logos are trademarks and/or
registered trademarks of Scholastic Inc.

First published in the US by Scholastic Inc, 2019
First published in the UK by Scholastic Ltd, 2020

Copyright © Dav Pilkey, 2019

The right of Dav Pilkey to be identified as the
author and illustrator of this work has been asserted by him.

ISBN 978 1407 19194 2
A CIP catalogue record for this book
is available from the British Library.

Printed in China
Papers used by Scholastic Children's Books are made
from wood grown in sustainable forests.

1 3 5 7 9 10 8 6 4 2

www.scholastic.co.uk

MIX
Paper from
responsible sources
FSC® C008047

CHAPTERS

For we are too deep. And too mature.
So true. So true!!!
As a very wise man* once said...
* Harold
"Enlightenment is not merely VoLition...
...but duty!"
Snork!
what?
You said "Butt doodie!"
HA HA HA HA HA HA HA HA HA HA HA H
HA

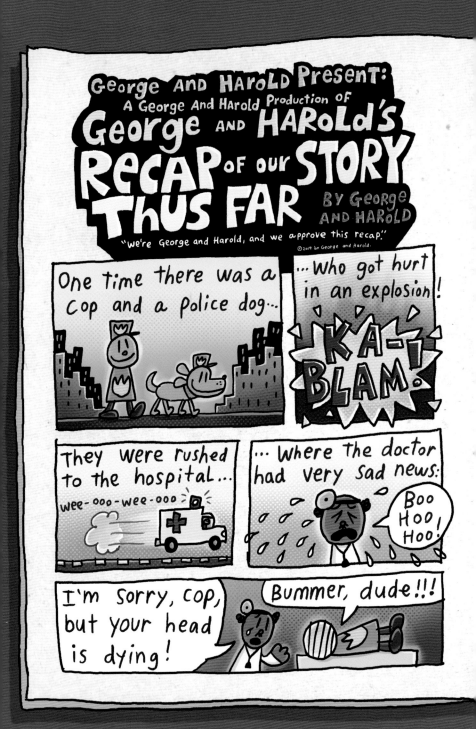

But Petey's evil heart is beginning to change...
...because of one little kitten.
Li'l Petey (very good-hearted)
Li'l Petey lives with Dog Man...
DOG MAN
...and their Re-markable Robot Pal, 80-HD.
Most of the time, they're a family...
...but sometimes, they're Superheroes.

Remember,

while you are flipping,
be sure you can see
the image on page 19
AND the image on page 21.

If you flip quickly,
the two pictures will
start to look like
one **Animated** cartoon!

Don't forget to
add your own
sound-effects!

Left
hand here.

Right
Thumb
here.

munch munch
What's it say, Chief?
Hey! It's from Yolay Caprese!!!
Chief
chew chew chew
Yolay Caprese
39 Glamorous Rd.
Hollywood, CA.
Dear Chief,
Ciao from Hollywood! We finally finished making the Dog Man Movie. Enclosed are twenty tickets to the red-carpet Premiere. See ya there!
Your pal,
Yolay Caprese

Right
Thumb
here.

64

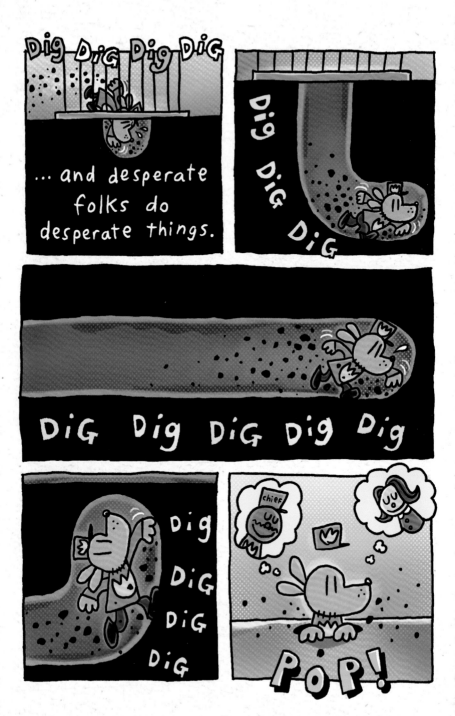

OH, No! This is worse than I imagined!!!

* Italian for: "My Peeps!!!"

88

99

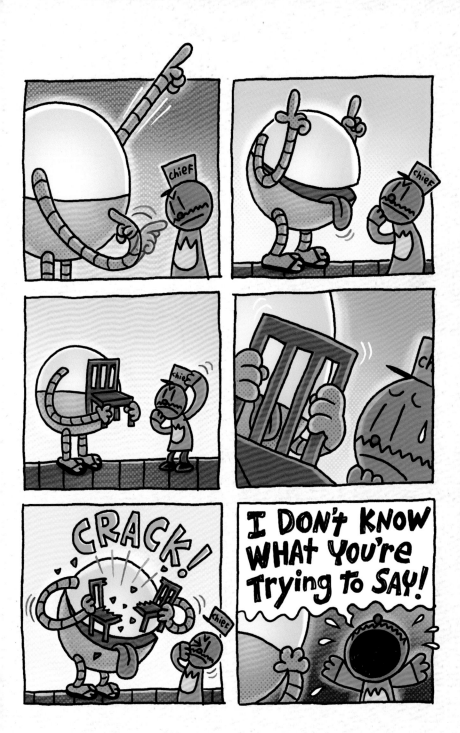

Meanwhile, Yolay, Sarah, and Zuzu were hot on the trail.
My investigative reporting skills led us to the seedy side of the city...
...And Zuzu's sniffing skills are picking up the scent...
SNIFF SNIFF SNIFF
NOW, I shall use my charismatic "People skills" to get clues!
Watch this!!!

Right
Thumb
here.

129

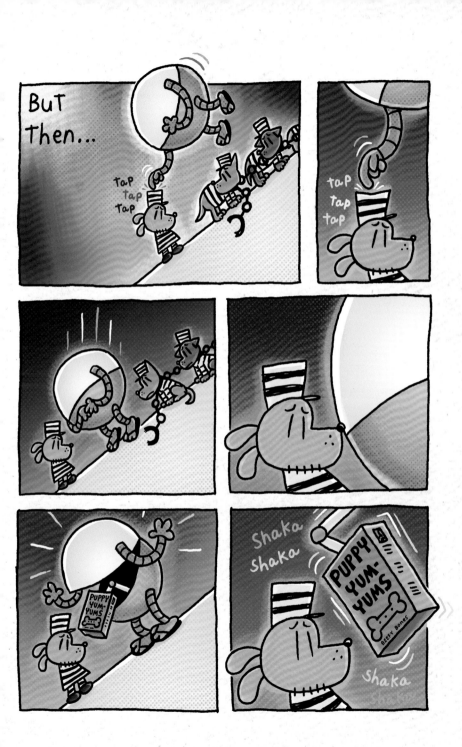

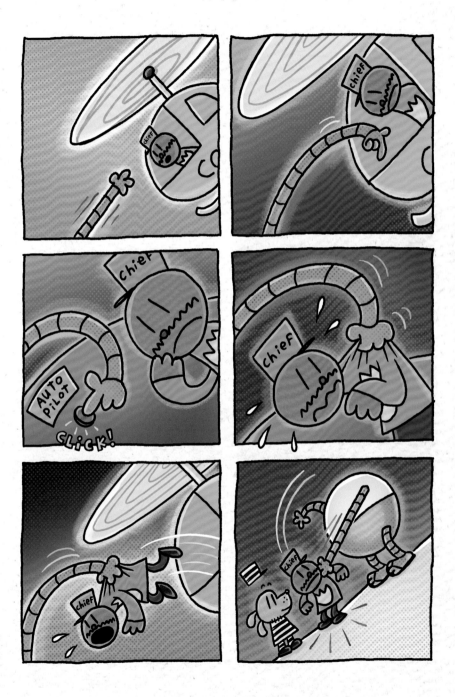

CHAPTER 9

DOG MAN
The MAJoR Motion PicTuRe

Sam E. Hamilton Presents
A GASSY BeHemoth Animation Production
DOG Man: The MAJoR Motion PicTuRe
Featuring the Vocal talents of: YoLay Caprese • Scooter McRibs
Ding-Dong Magoo • And Samson J. Johnson as "Chief"

soundtrack available on
Gassy Behemoth 8-tracks

DOGGY Surround Sound

K-9 suitable for canines
some material may be too intense for Humans

150

STOP, YOU CRAZY IMPOSTOR!

CRASH!

Now to find out who this impostor Really is!

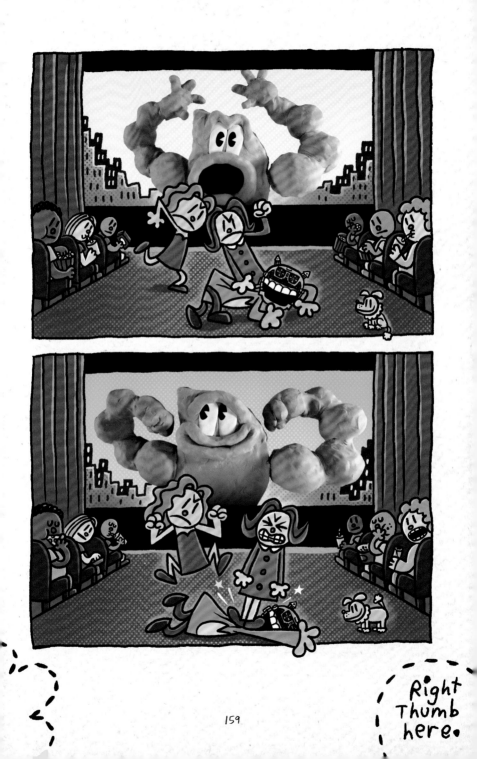

Right
Thumb
here.

166

174

175

177

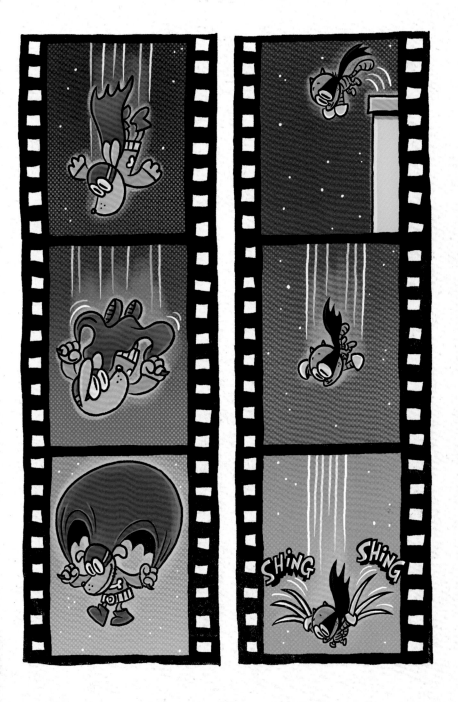

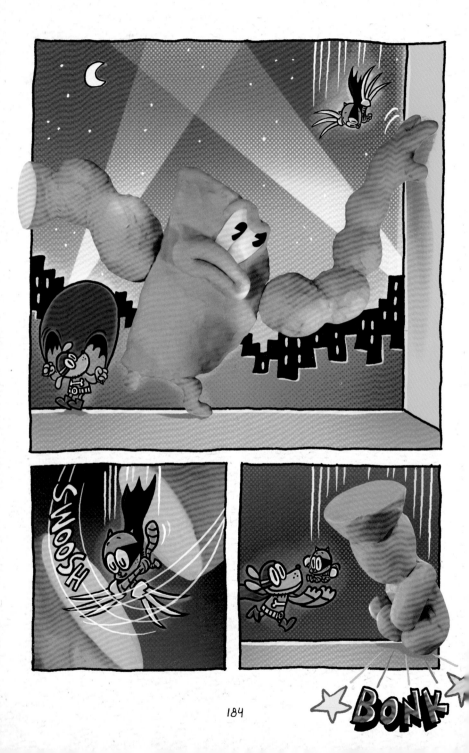

184

185

PLOP!

HEY!

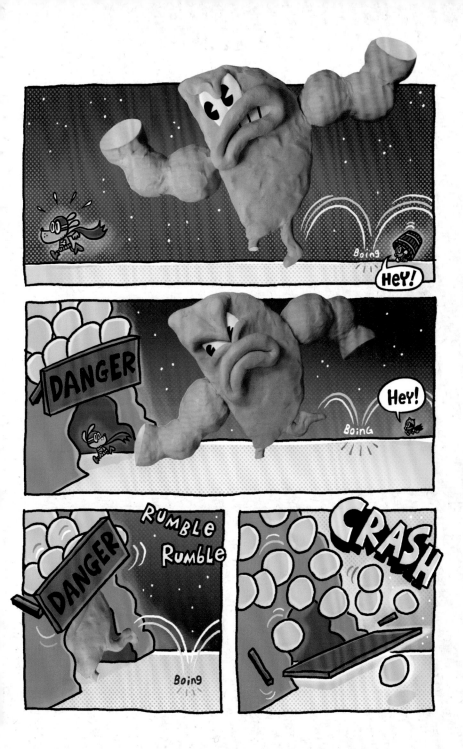

195

Right
Thumb
here.

199

200

Don't feel bad, Dog Man.

I've never told anybody this...

...but I feel like a misfit, too.

HeY! So do **I**! Every day!!!

SUPA BUDDIES SAVE THE DAY:

The *Supa* Buddies kept everybody safe during last night's tragic fire. Cat Kid, the leader of the *Supa* Buddies, was sad afterward because he forgot to sing their theme song (which he made up) during the big brawl. "Next time I'll remember better," said Cat Kid.

THE FLEAS: WHERE ARE THEY NOW?

The FLEAS
(artist's depiction)

ey the Cat

Nobody knows the whereabouts of Piggy, Crunky, and Bub (AKA The FLEAS). They were last seen in the burning movie theater, but then they disappeared.

"I just don't know what happened to them," said Petey the Cat as he scratched himself inside his jail cell this morning. "They just *vanished*," he continued, scratching again and again. "Where could they be?" he asked again, scratching vigorously

Menu ☰

HERO DOGS FIND FOREVER HOMES

The seven former inmates at Dog Jail were pardoned this morning for being heroes at last night's fire. They were immediately adopted by a buncha nice families and stuff, and are living happily ever after and stuff.

COMEUPPANCE

This morning, three meanies were pulled out of a stinky hole in the ground. During the rescue, the rope broke and they fell back into the hole a buncha times. It was awesome.

DOG MAN IS GO!

Reports are pouring in about an ALL-NEW Dog Man adventure that is coming your way. It will be available soon, but you should start bugging your parents, librarian, and/or bookseller about it now, just to be safe.

The title of this top secret book can now be revealed in this exclusive scoop:

The new book will be called DOG MA ᷍ !!! You heard it here first, folks!

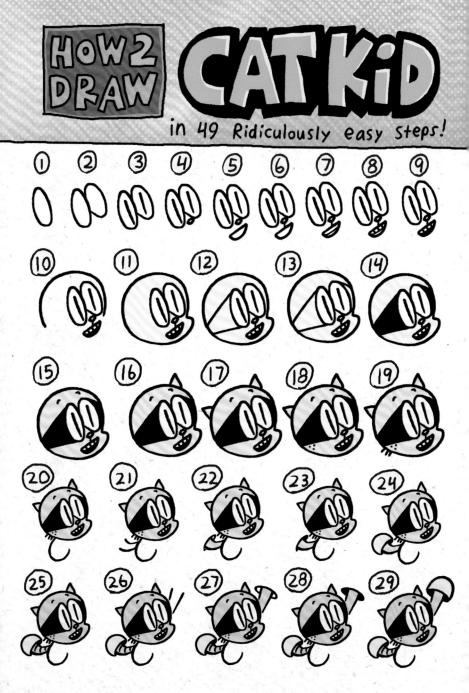

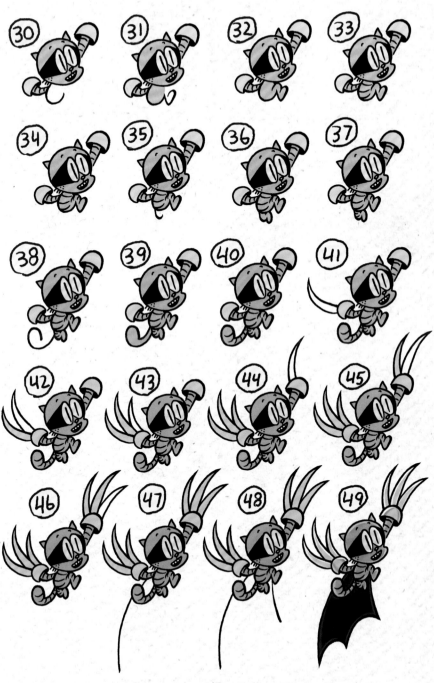

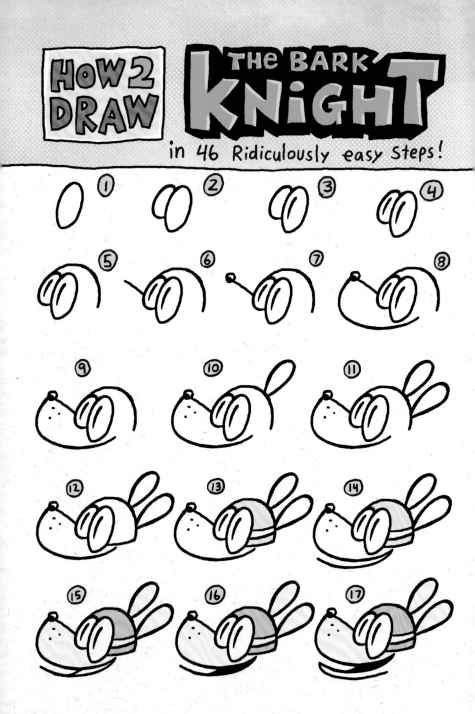

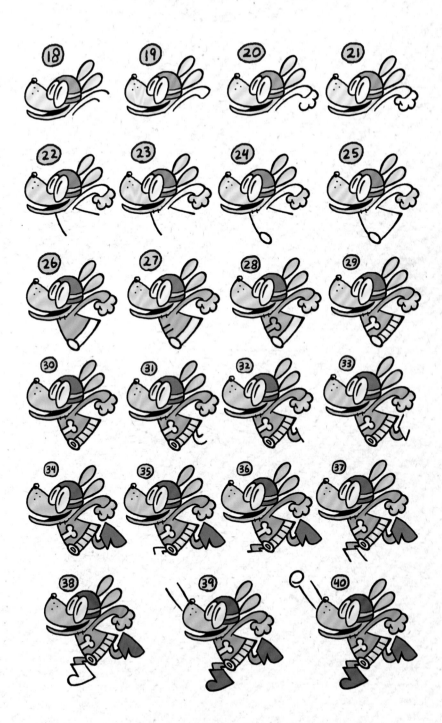

"A fun introduction to chapter books."
— *SCHOOL LIBRARY JOURNAL*

ABOUT THE AUTHOR-ILLUSTRATOR

When Dav Pilkey was a kid, he suffered from ADHD, dyslexia, and behavioral problems. Dav was so disruptive in class that his teachers made him sit out in the hall every day. Luckily, Dav loved to draw and make up stories. He spent his time in the hallway creating his own original comic books.

In the second grade, Dav Pilkey created a comic book about a superhero named Captain Underpants. His teacher ripped it up and told him he couldn't spend the rest of his life making silly books.

Fortunately, Dav was not a very good listener.

ABOUT THE COLORIST

Jose Garibaldi grew up on the South Side of Chicago. As a kid, he was a daydreamer and a doodler, and now it's his full-time job to do both. Jose is a professional illustrator, painter, and cartoonist who has created work for many organizations, including Nickelodeon, MAD Magazine, Cartoon Network, and Disney. He is currently working as a visual development artist on THE EPIC ADVENTURES OF CAPTAIN UNDERPANTS for DreamWorks Animation. He lives in Los Angeles, California, with his wonder dogs, Herman and Spanky.